Sorry I can't stay for more fun and games.

Oooh! My head—

Did he see the guns?

No—we rushed him before he could spot anything.

That night . . .

My info was correct, there is some big gang action coming off at the TT races. My long journey was really necessary.

A 'bug' bolt is called for. I need to hear more

We pull the 'big one' during the race. No one will expect it. The casino job should be worth best part of a million . . .

The casino does great trade during the TT fortnight. But 'best part of a million'? How?

One way to find out—go upstairs and hang around until it happens. I'll know those gents with the guns . . .

At the Casino . . .

Here goes my first line! I'll fire a recoil bolt next.

5

And up I go—it's as good as being a bird!

A grandstand view of the Casino. I'll spend the night here. Those goons might strike tonight. But tomorrow morning surely is a better time.

They're away!

Next morning—the start of the Senior TT.

Meanwhile, masked and using two-way radio links, the gangsters were on the move.

We hit the Casino while everyone's watching the TT race.

Oh! The arrival of baddies! Now we're in business. Just as I thought.

Down I go! I'm missing the big race, but business before fun. There are other races any way—

X-Bow soon caught up.

One against five—but I've a shot for any occasion.

This calls for twin-bolts—and an overhead shot!

What— A net!

Three down— two to go!

Make for the circuit! He daren't touch us there.

That crossbow character is a madman!

Meanwhile—back in the Casino.

Police! We've been robbed! Men on motorbikes . . . someone with a crossbow tried to help us. On a bike too . . .

A slip-road let the crooks on to the circuit.

What is going on?

Lunatics, cutting in!

X-Bow closed in.

I daren't use my bow and risk a race pile-up . . .

X-Bow overtook a competitor in mid-air.

Fantastic! It's like in films.

I've forced him out—right into these waiting cops. Only one more to go!

I'll make a break for it here!

We're in the open now, bad lad, so—

Down goes number five! Got 'em all!

Five minutes later the police arrived—and X-Bow left.

Do we let that one go?

Yes, we know about him—he's on our side in his own way.

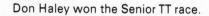

Don Haley won the Senior TT race.

I'm glad that X-Bow character wasn't competing. He would have been tough to beat. Where is he anyway?

That night . . .

Hi, lads. You're the enthusiasts who really make motor cycling. You put your bikes before your own comfort. Buy yourselves some tents.

I collected my reward money from one of the loot bags. The casino won't mind, I'm sure.

**The End**

10

13

16

# DODDS DOWN UNDER

JOE DODDS was an English boy who lived with his grandfather, Ernie Dodds, in Australia. They had left England to run a haulage business which had been left to Ernie by a war-time comrade. When he was not helping with the trucks, Joe was a keen angler.

*Gosh, what a great morning for fishing! No traffic about, either—I might even have the river to myself!*

Suddenly—

*Yeah-man! Ma Sugar says Yeah—Yeah-man—!*

*Good grief! What did I say about no traffic? I hope that bloke stays well away from where I'm heading!*

Joe needn't have worried — his favourite fishing spot was deserted except for some herons.

*This is the life!*

Later . . .

Came another interruption . . .

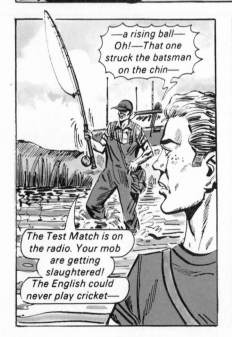

# TALL TALES *from the* DEEP

THIRTY FOUR, THIRTY FIVE, PHEW—

The largest fish is the whale shark. One was caught in Siam measuring 60 ft. 9 in. (18.5 m.)

A sailfish was timed at 68.1 m.p.h. off Florida.

FRYING TONIGHT

Electric eels in the rivers of South America, can discharge 650 volts.

The four-winged flying-fish can do a "long jump" of 3640 ft. (1110 m.)

A swordfish has been known to penetrate 22 in. (56 cm.) of a ship's timbers, which means it reached 57.6 m.p.h. to do it.

WANTED

Beware the Stonefish, found in the Indian and Pacific Oceans. A touch from the spines of its fins can be fatal.

# PEPPER MINTER HE'S HOT STUFF!

LEN MINTER, the Dalton City footballer, had been appointed player-manager of the Third Division side. He was nicknamed Pepper and had transformed the team into a hard-hitting, match-winning side, through example and with various gimmicks. But now as they attacked against Rumsey United . . .

*Poor Charlie, that's a nasty one—*

*Penalty, ref.*

*How are you, Charlie?*

*A bit sore, but I'll be okay, boss.*

Young Fred Casson was the penalty-taker . . .

*Well done, son. That's how you've been taught to take 'em!*

Terry Tracy was sports reporter on the Dalton Sentinel.

*Great goal! Hey, Billy, let's have a pie to celebrate!*

Billy Batters' pies were famous locally

*One of your pies will make the day, Billy.*

*Thanks, Terry. Every goal the lads score seems to make the fans want more of my pies. It's great!*

Great goal, Tony.

A three-one win for the City. Leaving the Press box Tracy met Harcourt Harvey the famous sports columist.

A national paper reporter covering a match in Dalton! What brings you here, Harvey?

There's maybe a story in the way this chap Minter is having such success lately. He seems to be full of ideas.

That's eight wins in a row, Minter. What's your secret?

Just put the best young player-manager in Britain in charge of a bunch of talented youngsters and you get an unbeatable combination.

Pepper never missed a chance to make news . . .

Take the lads a pie each, Billy. They've earned their pies today.

That's publicity talk, Minter. I want facts—your training techniques, how you give the players the urge to win—

That's our secret. Billy Batters' famous pies give my lads extra drive and energy.

Come off it, Minter. You can't tell me that pies can make players into better footballers!

Next day . . .

Harvey's used your pie story as a big joke, Pepper.

Daily Gazette **SPORT** PAGE

THE SECRET WEAPON OF FOX'S GIANT-KILLERS — BILLY BATTER'S MEAT PIES.

Sure, Terry, but it gets my team talked about and that gives the lads a boost! That's the whole idea.

In the trainer's room . . .

Sorry, but Bill here won't be ready for the match against Warbridge on Wednesday.

That's tough. Charlie's off too. We'll have to field reserves for that evening match.

The following Wednesday . . .

Don't loiter, lads! Go for the ball!

A goal given away! The lads have lost their rhythm.

27

Later . . .

Nut-megged! Cheeky stuff—but that's the way to beat the big 'un.

To me now, Bill. Switch the attack!

Just the job. We've caught them napping.

A inside pass from Pepper, and . . .

Great goal! Give the lads more pies, Pepper!

Whether it was the effect of Billy Batters' pies or not, the City played inspired stuff. All the rhythm and understanding returned. United were kept under constant pressure.

Pepper finished the scoring with a spectacular goal.

Good goal, Pepper.

Later . . .

Billy Batters' pies seemed to do the trick, Pepper.

The lads needed something to take their minds off the poor first half. If they believe in magic pies, who am I to argue?

The sports writers had fun with the pie story—but one man was taking no chances. Dan Morgan was manager of Ganton Rovers, the team Dalton City were to meet in the fourth round of the F.A. Cup.

To stop a striker scoring you cut off his supply—and that's just what I'm going to do with Batters' pies. If they work with Minter they could work with us.

BILLY BATTERS' MAGIC PIES!

PIES HELP CITY VICTORY

Early Saturday morning, in Billy Batters' pie shop . . .

I'll buy every pie in the shop. Put them in the van outside!

Certainly, sir.

And what about that lot? I said every pie in the shop!

Well—er—these are for the City football team!

Listen! My brother is head of the Health Department in the city. He would find a reason to close this place down—if you don't do as your told!

OK, mister, I'll sell 'em to you!

Danny Day, of Dalton City came in . . .

Hi, Billy. I've come to pick up our pies.

Sorry, Danny. This gent's just bought all the pies.

Hey, I know you! You're Morgan, of Ganton! Well, of all the dirty tricks!

You've one pie left Billy—I'll have it!

You can have it. One pie won't go far among eleven players!

Ganton had a reputation for being a ruthless team . . .

Crafty beggar! Their players shield each other from the ref. while they do the dirty stuff!

The Dalton City defence was obstructed—and Ganton scored.

Danton are tough, and they're crafty with it! It's nearly halftime. I'll have to think of something to beat their tactics—

Ganton kept up the rough stuff.

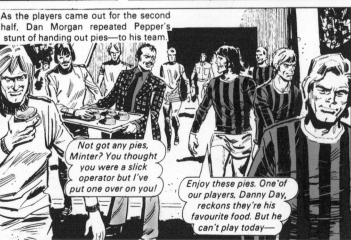

As the players came out for the second half, Dan Morgan repeated Pepper's stunt of handing out pies—to his team.

Not got any pies, Minter? You thought you were a slick operator but I've put one over on you!

Enjoy these pies. One of our players, Danny Day, reckons they're his favourite food. But he can't play today—

# POP LOLLY

Pop Lolly was the crossing controller at Highfield School. His lollipop could work magic. One day—

Har! Har! That fixed him!

Hello! What are these louts doing in the allotments?

Pop, look what these two did to my prize blooms for this afternoon's show!

H'mm. Got any seedlings, Harry?

These can never be ready for today, Pop.

Let's see what Lolly can do, Harry.

Hey, presto!

Gosh, your lollipop is magic, Pop.

Lolly just speeded things up a bit, Harry. Try these at the flower show.

Hello! A rope stretched across the path!

Lolly acted like a TV set.

Now, where are these two louts? Ah! I see—thanks, Lolly.

They're waiting to trip up someone. We'll fix 'em, Lolly.

One rubber hose, and one magic Lolly—

—makes two louts think they are being attacked by a snake!

Waaagh! Help!

I'm not coming near these allotments again!

A snake chasing two worms, Lolly!

32

It says "Put it in a hollowed-out turnip and watch for me. The Limpng Man."

The Limping Man! He's one of our top agents!

Later.

These papers contain everything we've learned about the new German factories. Let's hope the Limping Man will find them useful.

Well, a man who thought up that way of contacting us can do anything.

Two days later the prisoners were marched to a public bath-house outside the camp.

Ho, there! Do you want me to strike you again, British pig?

There he is again, sir. Now's your chance.

How do you like that, you rascal?

Good shot, Colonel!

Many thanks, Britisher. This will do nicely for my dinner.

Well done! That'll teach these British pigs.

Back in his rented room Spencer studied the contents of the turnip.

Most of this stuff we already know, but this news about the tank factory at Detmonden is useful. A super tank, eh? I'd better check on it.

Next day, Spencer visited the local Army barracks.

A volunteer, Herr Major. He is tired of sick leave. He wants a job.

Ach, the fellow who attacked the British colonel. We can find a place for one with such spirit. Where's your home?

I belong to Detmonden, Herr Major. Surely there is some war-work a cripple can do!

Detmonden, eh? Excellent. They need a watchman at their tank-testing ranges.

The following week, at Detmonden.

Your job is to record every vehicle using the range and to report damage. You will see secret equipment, but— remember— careless talk, or taking photographs is death!

This range is in use all day but I've seen nothing interesting this week so far. The tanks are Standard Mark Three and Four types.

A week later.

Ah, something new! And what a powerful gun! I must have a closer look at this.

What a panzer! Look at the tracks! They seem as wide as a barn door.

Ach! It is the new watchman. He hasn't seen a Tiger before.

Take a good look! This is the panzer that is going to win the war for Germany.

What a gun! I'm glad I'm not an enemy tank-man!

Ja! We can hit hard! Also the hull is low, making it a difficult target.

What a wonderful machine! If only I were not a cripple— I would be proud to serve in a panzer like that.

Yes, it takes a fit man to serve in a Tiger. But you may look inside the turret. I'll help you up.

Look at the size of the gun's breech! And all those instruments! I've never seen anyting like it!

Ja! The enemy would give much to see what you are seeing, my friend.

That finishes my job here. The German war industry is about to lose a watchman.

A fortnight later, Spencer, using secret routes, returned to London.

It's good to see you back, Spencer. Did you have any luck with those special prisoners-of-war?

Yes, sir. I've brought back a full report.

Photographs of a new heavy German tank. How did you get them? You couldn't risk pointing a camera at it!

No, but nobody minded me pointing my crutch at it. I'd a miniature cine-camera inside the leg and here is the film.

When the film had been developed.

Magnificent, Spencer! From this film we'll be able to calculate every detail of this new German tank.

Well, sir, there are times when a cripple's wooden crutch is a better war weapon than a machine-gun!

The End

# KING COBRA

**MORNING BUGLE**

**KING COBRA TURNS CROOK. FAMOUS LAWMAN TAKES FORTUNE FROM BANK**

Nigel Brent the Bugle's photographer was in luck. He was in the National Bridgewater Bank at the moment of the robbery.

**N**EXT morning, at a national English newspaper, ace reporter Bill King got a visit from his editor.

Bill, we've been scooped by the Morning Bugle. Biggest story in years. King Cobra turns crook. They've even got a picture of the bank robbery.

MORNING
KING COBRA TURNS CROOK.
LAWMAN TAKES FORTUNE.

Brent lucky to be there? No, that is too much to believe. The crooks must have wanted Nigel Brent to take this picture, or they would have clobbered him.

Later, at Brent's flat.

I think Brent should have a visit from the REAL King Cobra.

I know Brent's out on a job because I checked. I only need a couple of minutes in here.

Bill King's amazing secret was that he was the real King Cobra, world-famous crook-catcher extraordinary.

When Brent came home, he received several phone calls and then—

Brent? This is K.C. We're making the share-out tonight. Stonewalls at ten o'clock.

I'll be there in twenty minutes.

A tiny bug in the phone and I'll pick up anything said on it on my special car radio.

**Stonewalls? Sounds like the name of a house. It can't be far away judging by the time now.**

Bill soon tracked down Stonewalls, a large house. With him he took a cricket bag, identical to the one in the newspaper photo.

**Someone is inside, but there's only one car. I've got some time before the others arrive.**

**I've hit the jackpot—it's my double, the fake King Cobra! He's getting the bank haul out of that safe!**

King Cobra swooped.

The imposter never knew what hit him.

**The safe's open. I've got to work fast.**

39

41

Outside, King Cobra spread his special nylon wings and leaped on to the balustrade.

*I'll have to get airborne to stop these two.*

RAMSON & CO. TRANSPORT

King Cobra glided down on to the van.

*It's King Cobra! He's coming through the windscreen.*

*King Cobra has stopped the crooks, but look, there he goes.*

*That's ruined their getaway. Now I'll make myself scarce.*

*We've got the fake King Cobra and all his gang.*

*But the real King Cobra has vanished—he always does when he's finished a job.*

Later.

*Great stuff, Bill. You've scooped all our rivals on this King Cobra story.*

*We've got to let the world know there's only one King Cobra—and that he's on the side of law and order.*

**The End.**

43

CAPTAIN Smith and Sergeant Jones, of the British Army, were experts at handling awkward situations world-wide . . . such as when four members of the Manfuha Brethern, a Middle East terror gang, were trapped in the New York penthouse of the Tollinger Building, with their kidnap victim, an Arab oil minister.

*Order the helicopter to go away—or I set off the explosive fastened to Shaikh al-Maari.*

*I'm ordering him off right now, Captain Abu. It's some newspaper men trying to get a scoop.*

In the helicopter were Smith & Jones.

*They are spooking, Smith. Get outa there.*

*Not to worry, Chief Hauk. Only a few seconds now.*

*Jones is making his shot.*

**PHUT!**

Smith and Jones were met on the PANAM 'copter pad by Hauk, Chief of the New York City Police.

*The meeting is set up down in the operations room, boys. The Feds, army and air force brass, the city fathers—and none of them is happy.*

*We'll try to cheer them up, Chief Hauk. That infra-red beam is now placed on Tollinger Building.*

# ПITH and JONES

Gentlemen, you can see that the top of a skyscraper is hard to check, even with modern spy technique. But we are satisfied the penthouse roof is the one blind spot.

But your President is for it!

Yes, folks, up in the Tollinger Building the drama continues. The ruthless gunmen who seized Shaikh al-Maari, are demanding a ransom of ten million dollars and an aircraft . . .

New York at night.

ABC

The Naval Air Station, Jamaica Bay.

Can I help out in any way?

Maybe so, but your plan of a parachute drop— I'm against it.

Thanks, but we have our own weapons and ram-air 'chutes.

Smith and Jones took off . . .

In free fall .

Police Chief Hauk commanded the Ops Room.

Nearing touchdown! Time for that diversion.

Gimme that clear phone line to the penthouse.

Captain Abu, the President agrees to your terms. Free Shaikh al-Maari and you get your ten million dollars and an aircraft out of the country.

We're down.

Outside the gangsters' room.

That 'phone call worked. They're together—off guard.

Not quite, Jones.

Look what that man's holding— a radio beam detonator.

Smith made a radio call.

Chief, another diversion or the Shaikh gets exploded.

Open up that penthouse line again.

Seconds later—the penthouse . . .

The telephone. They call me again, brothers.

RINNG!

47

Suddenly . . .

*Abu! What is that strange light on your face?*

Abu went down . . . and dropped the detonator.

Jones tossed in a stun-bomb . . .

. . . and they went in shooting.

RATATAT!

*It's over, Your Excellency.*

Next morning at Kennedy International Airport . . .

*It's over, folks. Our own city cops stormed the Tollinger penthouse, shot down the gunmen and freed Shaikh al-Maari . . .*

*A spot of leave now, Jones.*

*Yes, sir. I wonder what the weather's like in England?*

**The End**

# Bernard's St. Bernard

YOUNG Bernard Briggs ran his own scrap-metal business, but life became more complicated when a friend was injured and Bernard took on Montague of Manningham, the biggest, clumsiest St Bernard ever. It was in for a local show.

*There, you look a treat, Monty. Stay here and keep clean. I've got work to do outside.*

But when Bernard next looked at his watch . . .

*Gosh, I'm late! And I've got a lot to fit in—*

*Monty . . ? Where are you? Oh, oh, that window—*

*Oh, no! Burying a bone!*

*You great, stupid lump! I'm short of time and you get yourself all dirty!*

A crash beauty course followed.

*That's the best I can do, but you look not too bad. Let's go, Monty. I've no time for lunch now.*

Shortly afterwards . . .

*There are cats and birds as well as dogs in for this show. I hope they keep them well apart!*

But this had been taken care of by the committee.

What a load of pot-lickers here today, Monty.

What a superb specimen of a dog. It's amazing what can turn up at these small shows.

Later . . .

Winner of the St Bernard class—and Best Dog in Show—Montague of Manningham!

Hooray, that last minute bath must have done the trick.

We want a picture of all three Show Champions together.

I hope Monty likes cats!

Monty liked everyone, including cats . . .

Keep that animal away, young man. My Arabella hates dogs.

Gronph, gronph.

Sptt—sptt!

Yeeeoww!

Revenge was what Monty was after now . . .

Monty! Come back!

Oh, my poor Arabella!

The fugitive cat raced into the cage-bird room.

A cat! Get hold of it, quick!

And a dog! We're in trouble!

What a shambles!

The tearoom was the next to be "visited".

Monty! Here, Monty!

All that grub—ruined! Oh, Monty—

Sptttt! Sptt!

Woof—woof—woof!

Now the birds are loose, Monty—

Joey! My Joey's gone out the window —and he was champion!

Monty and the cat were eventually caught. Then the birds were secured. Bernard, meanwhile, got a roasting from the show officials.

Your dog has done at least £30 worth of damage. That budgie alone was worth ten pounds. You are responsible!

Thirty quid! You'll have to wait until Monday. Give me a chance—

Right, Monday it is. But we'll keep the dog as hostage.

You can do that! He's not mine to start with!

The officials were adamant.

Woof—woof—woof!

So long for now, Monty. How am I going to raise thirty quid?

**B**ERNARD went off to the local recreation park. He was goalkeeper for Manningham Youth Club.

*Bernard, where's the dog that was going to be our mascot?*

*It's a long story. Right now I have to get changed!*

The match was against Cleghampton Youth, a notable Cup-fighting team. At first Bernard was kept busy.

Manningham fought their way back into the game.

*GOAL! That's better, Manningham—we're on our way now!*

*A budgie—here in the park? Hey, would it be the one that escaped?*

*Pretty Joey, 6 Maple Avenue. Joey, Joey, Joey.*

*It is Joey! Here's a chance to chop ten quid off that bill!*

*Hey, look out, Bernard!*

*Gotcha!*

*Must hold it gently. Don't want to hurt the bird.*

*Bernard! Bernard!*

*Not to worry! Now take it through, Dave! They're wide open.*

Well done, lads. That's a bonus—ten quid saved, and a goal scored!

Hey, any of you blokes got a small box that'll hold a budgie till the match is over?

One of the spectators obliged, but meantime two show officials were taking Monty home—

Seems to have settled down now, doesn't he?

But Monty saw a game of football in progress and, because he associated this with Bernard, he became restive.

Stop it, dog. Get back there at once.

These lights are at red—get him under control before they change!

Next moment . . .

Get off, you brute, get off! Oooh, he weighs a ton . . .

I can't drive like this. Take him out at your side then get him into the back.

When the door was opened . . .

Hold him . . .

Too late—he's gone!

The lights changed.

Wait—I'll go after him!

We can't wait here! Let the brute go—we'll catch him later.

It was the second half of Bernard's match, with Manningham 2-0 in the lead when, suddenly . . .

Woof-woof-woof-woof!

Monty . . . Oh, no . . . not now!

Quick, Jim—get it over . . . !

WOOOOOOOF!

YEEE-AAARGH!

The Cleghampton striker took his chance.

Sp-splutter! Get off me, you great slobbering twit—get off me, I say . . . !

Near full time, a final sortie by Cleghampton—

Saved, Bernard!

A quick clearance went to the Manningham striker—

Offside, ref . . .

Play the whistle— get after him!

—who left the defence behind.

It was all over a few minutes later.

Great work, Bernard —you spotted that opening a treat!

Monty deserves the credit, the big soft lump.

After the match, Bernard went to 6 Maple Avenue, and his luck was in.

Thank you so much. I thought I'd never see Joey again. There's a ten pound reward.

Thanks, missus.

Well, that's ten quid off the bill. Now I'll sort out enough scrap to pay off the rest.

Later—

Phew, that was hot work but there should be about twenty quid's worth there for Bill the Scrappie.

I've been working while you've been feeding your fat face, Monty, but I suppose you'll want a walk. But just a short one tonight. I'm tired!

Monty didn't believe in short walks.

Come back, Monty!

The End

55

# Well, Doggone!

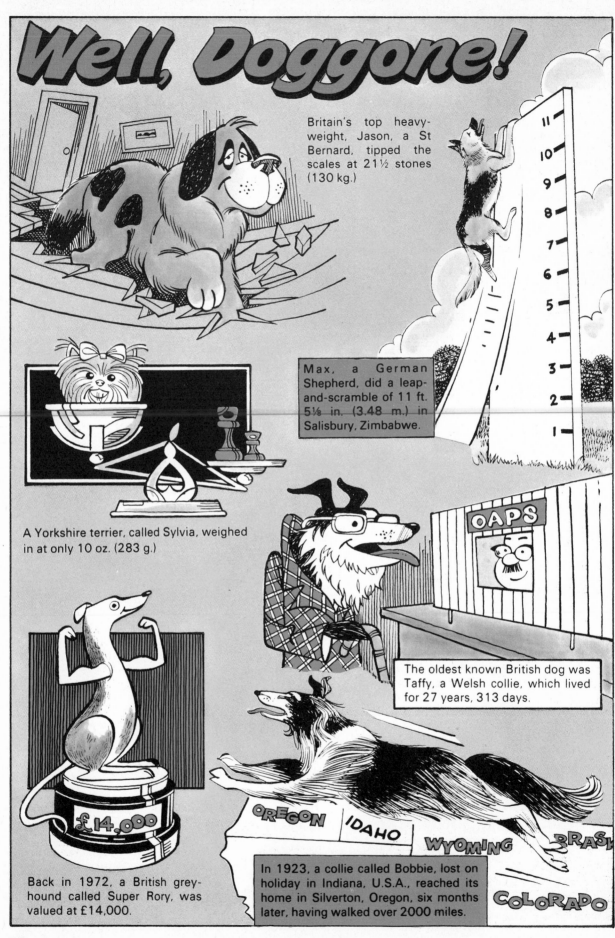

Britain's top heavyweight, Jason, a St Bernard, tipped the scales at 21½ stones (130 kg.)

Max, a German Shepherd, did a leap-and-scramble of 11 ft. 5⅛ in. (3.48 m.) in Salisbury, Zimbabwe.

A Yorkshire terrier, called Sylvia, weighed in at only 10 oz. (283 g.)

The oldest known British dog was Taffy, a Welsh collie, which lived for 27 years, 313 days.

Back in 1972, a British greyhound called Super Rory, was valued at £14,000.

In 1923, a collie called Bobbie, lost on holiday in Indiana, U.S.A., reached its home in Silverton, Oregon, six months later, having walked over 2000 miles.

There were other lucky charms aboard that night—as "Professor" Gibbs, the navigator found out.

What's happened to your flying boots, Skipper? The sole's hanging off one—

Just wear and tear, Prof! These were the pair I got on joining up! They've been lucky for me! We could do with a bit of luck.

The take-off was normal . . . for J for Jonah.

We've clipped those trees again!

The day that we miss them, I'll start to worry!

Skipper to Sparky . . . what's that squeaking coming over the intercom?

Dunno, sir. I'll check.

"Sparky" Watts, the radio operator checked all his instruments.

My equipment's OK, sir.

It's going to be annoying listening to that squeak all night.

Oh, sorry, sir, about the squeaking. It's Lucky, my mouse!

58

A ball of black fur exploded from the front turret.

What's that . . . ?

Look out . . . Squeaky—

Tompuss! Here, Tompuss!

What the blazes is Tompuss?

It's the sergeant's mess cat, Skipper. Black cats are lucky, so . . .

This one won't be if I catch it! It's torn my charts!

The chase hurtled into the radio cabin.

A mouse—and a cat! Get off!

Sparky fell off his stool.

Gah! I'm falling—

His silk scarf snagged, and tightened and tightened . . .

Uuuurrrgh! Choking . . .

Prof Gibbs lent a hand.

*Hold still, Sparky! The knot has gone iron tight—*

Finally . . .

*Phew! A present from my Aunt Mary! She said it would be lucky! Bah!*

The mouse found a hole underneath the main spar and the cat sat at the hole. Skipper Drake asked for a course check from Gibbs.

*You need ninety-one degrees, Skipper.*

The skipper adjusted the course, but . . .

*We still need ninety-one degrees. Three more to the left!*

*I wish you'd make up your mind, Prof.*

*Another five degrees left, Skipper.*

*Something wrong with my compass! Of course— My lucky horseshoe is affecting it. Sorry, Skipper.*

61

Lonely saw the bomb-burst beneath them.

*Bullseye! Our lucky mascots are working!*

*Oh, oh! Enemy fighters coming up astern, Skipper!*

As Lonely fired his four machine-guns, the lucky medal was jolted from its hook . . .

. . . and it fouled the turret-turning gears.

*My turret's jammed! I can't train my guns round—*

Freddy Fox took up the defence of J for Jonah.

Then his lucky rabbit's foot fell into the breech of one of his guns.

*Gah! Now my guns are jammed!*

63

# CALAMITY CHAYNE — HE GETS HIS MAN – ALL WAYS!

Remember, Chayne, keep your eyes open. Nothing must be stolen.

Leave it to me, Inspector.

THERE was a big rodeo and stock show in Calamity Chayne's home-town, and the Mountie's Inspector wanted no law-breaking.

An easy job this time. Who would pinch a prize bull?

Suddenly . . .

Wow! It's Lariat Larsen, the cattle rustler.

I haven't kicked a Mountie for at least a month.

Good. I haven't lost the knack!

Yeeeowww!

Here's a fine bull, all on its—

Look out, below!

Do you mind?

Exercise is what I need.

No-o-o-o!

Moments later, in the show-jumping arena

—and here we have a surprise competitor. Look-at-him-go!

A high-jumping bull! What next!

The bull did a perfect round.

—and I bet it's the fastest time too!

At the finish . . .

From now on you're on your own, Mountie.

Where am I going now?

FINISH

—back in the bull's pen!

Oooh, my head! Where did that Mountie get to?

He soon found out.

You win this cup for the fastest clear round!

And you've caught Lariat Larsen! How do you do it, Chayne?

It's difficult to explain, sir.

65

Gosh! That lad has guts, diving at the steel-tipped boots of these miners!

THOUGH the Scarlet Hawks were one of the wealthiest clubs in the country, well able to pay high transfer fees if necessary, they also had a strong youth policy. Manager Tom Scott was always on the look-out for promising young players.

A poor clearance, but I can't blame him for getting the ball as far away from these hefty forwards as possible.

Scott paused to watch the scratch match.

What a great save! His hands are as safe as houses.

The pit-head hooter sounded.

I'm Tom Scott, manager of the Scarlet Hawks. What's your name, lad? I'd like you to play a trial for us.

I'm Bill Anderson. I've got a day off tomorrow, so I could call in then if that's OK. Got to run now or they'll be docking my pay.

The following morning, at the Hawks' ground.

This is Sam Soutar, our coach. Sam, meet Bill Anderson. He's come along for a try-out as a goalie.

Glad to meet you, son. Come on and I'll get you kitted out.

There you are, lad. Get changed and we'll see how you shape against some first-division shooting.

But I'm not a goalie. I'm a centre-forward. I only play in goal at the pit-head, where everybody has to take a turn.

It was as a keeper I saw you and it's as a keeper I want you.

Soon.

See what I mean, Sam? The lad's a natural in goal.

And look at those hands. They're as strong as a vice!

Cup Final day

Right, lads. All aboard for Wembley.

AARGH!

It's badly sprained. Bert can't possibly play today. Our goalies are jinxed—Fred Barnes with a broken finger last week and now this.

At Wembley

A last minute change in the Scarlet Hawks' team—Anderson in place of Hewitt in goal.

Who's Anderson?

Oh, no! I saw him once playing for the third team. He has feet like face flannels. He can't kick a ball to save his life!

Young Anderson showed no nerves on the great occasion.

You'll have to try harder than that, mate.

Look at the length of that throw. He may have flannel feet but there's nowt wrong with his hands!

You're right, Jim. Maybe his name is "Hands" Anderson, eh?

Bill was playing to strict orders — under no circumstances was he to kick the ball. The full-back took goal kicks and on other occasions Bill threw the ball out.

In an exciting, evenly-fought game the Hawks finally went into the lead with three minutes to go.

Goal!

Worlton Arsenal fought back and in the dying seconds of the game

Penalty, Ref.

What a finish! The last kick of the match. I can't bear to look.

Bill saved it! We've won! The ref has blown for full-time!

HANDS ANDERSON! HANDS ANDERSON!

Hear that Bill? They're shouting for you!

From then on, there was no looking back for "Hands" Anderson. The following season he made the first team position his own and by the end of the season he had also collected a couple of international caps. His kicking improved slightly, but his skill depended mainly on his strong hands and arms.

Although hailed by some as the greatest 'keeper the Hawks ever had, Bill still enjoyed a game in the outfield and often played at centre-forward in practice matches.

Bill also continued to work as a miner and it was as a miner that his strong hands and arms made the greatest save of his life.

*A pit prop has cracked. The roof will come down!*

*Come on, Ned. This is no place for us.*

*This is the danger spot. We'll be OK once we're past this.*

*AAARRGH!*

*Come on, Ned! The whole lot's going to go!*

*My knee's gone! Save yourself, Bill!*

*I'm not leaving you behind, Ned. Come on, I can't hold it much longer.*

Ned crawled clear, the roof collapsed.

*My arm!*

*Bill! Are you all right!*

Bill's arm was so badly injured it had to be amputated at the elbow. His days as a goalkeeper were over.

*It's a terrible blow, Bill, but the Hawks are good to their old players. They'll find you a job.*

*Ah, but it won't be the same. I enjoyed my football, even though I couldn't kick.*

*My stars! What a shot. Try that again!*

Bill did it again—and again.

*It's amazing! He couldn't kick before because he was always unbalanced. Now he's lost his arm his balance is perfect.*

Before long " Hands " Anderson was playing for the Scarlet Hawks again—at centre-forward!

*Welcome back, Hands. Go out there and show them.*

*It's not " Hands " any longer. It's " Lefty " Anderson now.*

Letty went on to break the club's scoring record.

*What a goal! And to think he used to be the player who couldn't kick a ball.*

" Lefty " became the first player ever capped by England both as a goalkeeper and a centre-forward.

**The End.**

# WILLIE THE WINNER

"Phew! Another sackful of prizes won by your son, Mrs Wynn."

"I'm sorry for you, Postie. Where am I going to put this lot?"

YOUNG Willie Wynn had the amazing knack of winning any competition he entered—which was great, but it meant hard work for Postman Perkins delivering Willie's sacks of winnings.

"Poor old Postie. I'll give him one of my prizes! It might cheer him up!"

"Hey, Postie! Have this prize on me for all your hard work."

"Thanks, Willie. You open it."

"Postage stamps! What a present for a postie!"

"Sorry, Postie. Oops, and I've dropped them. Better pick 'em up."

Just then—

"Well done, laddie. As one of the organisers of the Keep-the-Town-Tidy campaign, I hereby award you a prize."

"Eh? A yo-yo! Oh, thanks, mister."

"I've got a cupboardful of yo-yos I've won. Ha! I'll give this one to the postie!"

"I used to be a dab hand with a yo-yo when I was a lad!"

"Hooray! He's smiling at last!"

"This is what I call my over-arm fling! Ooer . . ."

"Yikes. Clean through Mrs Jones' window."

70

**THE END**

# The COONSKIN GRENADIER

IN the Second World War, Zebadiah Flood quit the Great Smokies of Carolina to take up the duty awarded an ancestor—the Royal Warrant that made every Flood heir an Honorary Colonel of the posh English regiment, the Royal Grenadiers. The "real" colonel, Sir John Pelham, was forever aghast at Zeb's rather unorthodox methods. Now Zeb's mother read the latest letter from her son . . .

Hark'ee, hound dogs! Seems like young Zeb has gotten himself posted as a deserter—a runaway . . .

DEAR MAW,
COLONEL SIR JOHN THE BOSS OF POTOMAC BARRACKS GOT TOOK POORLY RIGHT AFTER ME AND ALEXANDER THE MASCOT COME BACK FROM FEUDIN' IN FURRIN PARTS WITH THEM SQUARE-HEAD YANKEES...

Don't you worry, Sir John. I'm here to run the regiment, and smarten up them guard mountings at Buckingham House and suchlike places.

Urrrh!

In the corridor Zeb met Sergeant-Major Minchin, a portly parade-ground warrior.

*You better call in the doc, Sarn't—Major. Sir John's swooned away again.*

*"I looked in on our Royal Grenadier guard at London Tower..."*

*What's all the commotion, cousin?*

*Evacuation of barracks and quarters, Honorary Colonel. Sappers have located an old unexploded German bomb.*

*"So everybody got cleared out—well, almost everybody..."*

*ALEXANDER! COME BACK.*

*Ah, there he is. I should have remembered, the mess steward supplies Alexander with bananas.*

*"That window opened into the office of the Officer Quarters..."*

*That's a mighty odd place to look for a bomb.*

*What bit me? Huh! Kinda early for skeeters.*

That was no mosquito . . . ooh!

Herr Major, he spied on you. I got him with my air pistol.

He must not be found here. Put him aboard the truck.

Inside the office again . . .

We have it, Herr Major—the secret of the hiding place.

Note it, and then tidy up. Nobody must suspect that safe has been opened.

" Those sappers worked fast . . . "

Follow me— forward!

Alexander did not mean to be left behind . . .

Achtung! There is now a large monkey in here.

Keep him quiet. We are approaching the checkpoint.

That bomb was a false alarm. The contact was an old drain under the hospital block.

Pass, friend.

Monkey, one whisper from you and I blow out your brains. Keep your paws up.

"Which is how I went missing . . ."

" . . . causing a heap of worry to my friends . . ."

Yessir—vanished. No trace of 'im, or the monkey.

Then after two days they must be posted as deserters, and are liable to be shot. Hooray!

HAW! HAW! SHOT! HAH! HAH!

Sir—go easy! You've gone red in the face.

"When I woke up, we were in an old quarry . . ."

Alexander, it seems there is something phoney about those sappers.

Herr Major, ich habe—

Speak English, Kurt. Even a word in Deutsch can betray us, should it slip out at the wrong time.

75

URGH!

...One up...

"Me and Alexander got ourselves unroped..."

Aha! This map is marked where them square-head Yankees is a'heading.

We'll borrow this here iron mule, Alexander.

"We took to the trail of them map marks..."

I must be seeing things...

Later, in the sickbay...

Sir John, the two deserters 'as been sighted in Cornwall.

Get after 'em with an armed detail. Sarn't Major. No—wait...

I'll assume command meself. Where's me uniform and me sword?

"Dusk found me and Alexander at the map marks..."

WHEEL JACK MINE, GOV'T PROPERTY

Now why would them Yankees be so interested in an ol' prospect hole?

There's the jalopy them varmints was using.

Guards—and it looks like they was skeeter-stung, like me.

" Then we heered this big noise . . ."

Two sappers came out of the mine shaft . . .

Kurt should be here by now. I shall feel happier for knowing our E-boat pick-up is on.

Agreed. Now, let us get the truck backed in and start loading.

Boys, there is something you ought to know about Kurt.

Ach! Was ist . . .

Kurt won't be coming.

" Me and Alexander snuck into that glory-hole . . ."

That steel door's been blasted. Looks like somebody didn't have a key.

The End.

79

# ARMY ODDITIES

The shortest war. In 1896, the British bombarded Said Khaled's palace in Zanzibar for 38 minutes, when he surrendered.

The largest catapult. Called onagers in old times, they could throw a 60 lb. missile about 500 yards.

The tallest soldier. V. Myllyrinne of the Finnish army measured 8 ft. 1¼ in.

The oldest army. Swiss Guards in the Vatican, in Rome, date back to 1506.

The longest range gun. The German Kaiser Wilhelm which bombarded Paris in World War I fired shells 76 miles.

76 MILES

The longest war. England and France fought almost continuously from 1338 to 1453, in what is known as the 100 Years War.

Deadly danger lurked nearby . . .

Ah—miss—driver move!

AAAAAH!

In we go, Willie! Knock 'em down!

Wow! It's crawlin' with Japs.

A piece of falling timber jammed the controls.

What's the matter, Willie? Somethin' got snarled up?

Back on the airstrip.

The little fireball's in trouble! Get to him!

Mighty Mouse! What's gone wrong?

Big Willie had run into a swampy area . . .

Now you're OK, Willie. Hey, we're really out in the wilds here.

Meanwhile . . .

Kill the natives! Capture the giant machine!

Banzai! Banzai!

Japs! Scatter, you guys!

Climb on to the great machine. Guard the Lord who guides it.

That's it, pile aboard, you guys.

That's it. Sock it to 'em!

Too many for us! We gotta make a fightin' retreat.

Okimbo pointed out a path, and Big Willie reversed down it . . .

You lead us out, buddie. Big Willie will follow.

Back at the base . . .

*A call from Mighty Mouse! Zeros on way!*

*We thought this place was clean. These Zeros must have come from another island!*

Afterwards . . .

*Contact Mighty Mouse. See if he can find out anything about the Zeros!*

Later . . .

*Big Willie wants to know where Devil Birds come from. They must be destroyed.*

*We find, master of giant one.*

The jungle had its own " telegraph ".

Thirty miles away . . .

*Americans think all aircraft on island destroyed.*

*We have fuel for many short trips.*

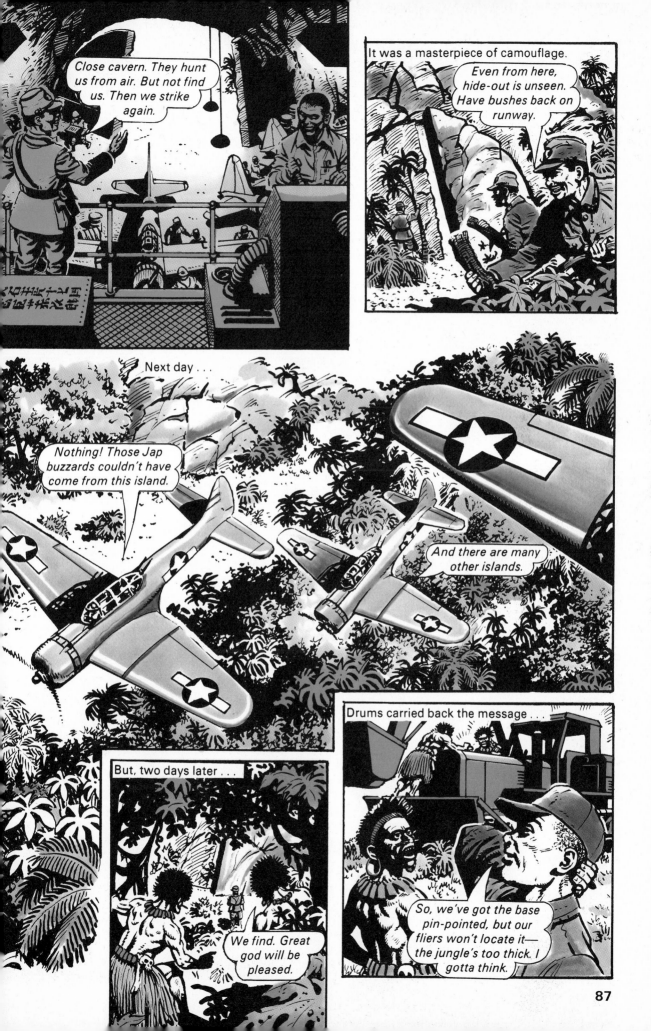

87

The start of a minor typhoon gave Mighty Mouse an idea.

We move! The great one leads us into battle.

I must be nuts!

Great Willie has magic over typhoon.

It stops chances of our engine being heard. And I doubt if many Japs will be scouting in this weather.

Later, at a rest break . . .

Oh Lord, we are near devil bird nest.

Good we'll get rolling again.

The sentries were soon dealt with . . .

NNNGH!

AAAAGH!

Here is entrance!

Let's seal it permanently. Hang on, Okimbo.

Big Willie heaved rocks, trees and earth over the hangar entrance.

# A Hard Day's Knight

I N days of old Sir Lansalot Fitzhorse was out seeking dragons to slay.

The dragon breathed fire—

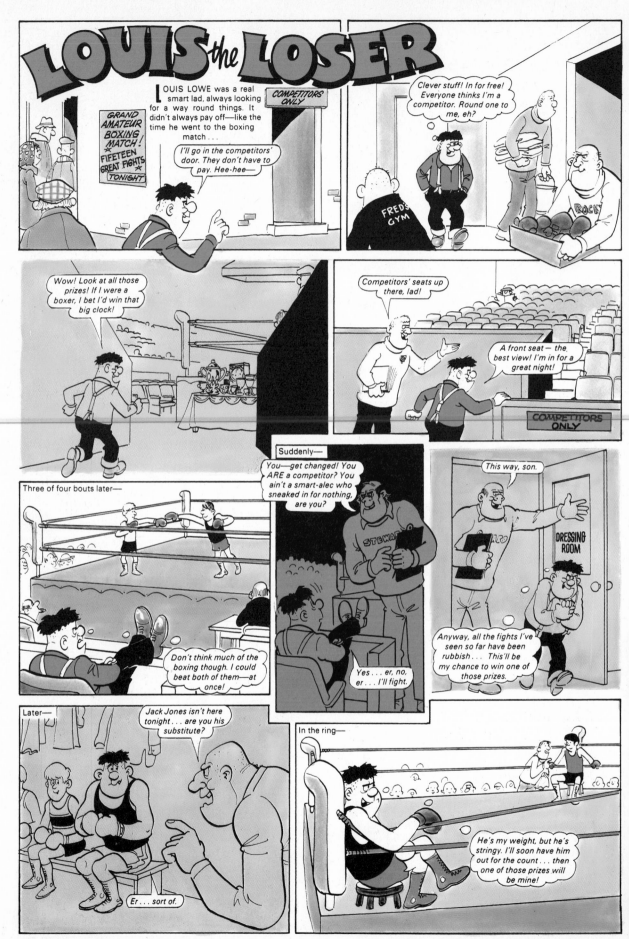

THE END

95

THE Flower Class corvette was introduced at the start of World War II when cheap easily-produced escort vessels were urgently needed. Called after flowers, these ships, developed from whaler design, were originally meant for coastal escort but often had to operate out in the Atlantic, on convoys.

The design allowed many small shipyards to build them. Fully-loaded they weighed around 1,160 tons, and were 205 feet long. Range was 2,630 miles at full speed of 16 knots. They had 50-70 depth charges and Asdic for submarine hunting. One 4 inch gun, one 2 pounder and other smaller armament for anti-aircraft defence.

# THEN...

# .. AND NOW

THIS is the USS Bronstein, an anti-submarine frigate introduced well after World War II. It is 371 feet long, has two boilers with geared turbines and can do 26 knots. The guns are two 3 inchers. Anti-submarine weapons are 8-tube Asroc launchers, two triple Mark 32 torpedo tubes, and two helicopters. The mast and the stack, the funnel, are combined in a " Mack ", which also carries the Radar gear. The sonar device, forward, is unique, as are the stem and side anchors.

Danny pitched up to within a foot. Harper's fifth shot was still well short.

Putt well to the right of the hole, mister.

It's a straight putt. I'm a member here, and I know. And call me sir.

The ball swung to the left. This caddie may look like a tearaway but he knows what he's talking about.

The fourth-hole was a dog-leg. It bent sharply to the right.

Aim on the line of the steeple, sir.

Harper's ball ended in the plantation.

Nonsense. I can cut the corner and save a stroke.

I warned him. Only a pro like you can carry that corner.

You know this course. Are you a local?

Never saw it before yesterday, mate. But I'm a caddie, it's my job to know the course.

As they searched for Harper's ball, the caddie told Danny how he went about things.

My name's Stu Price. I come to a course, I chat up the greenkeeper, I walk every inch of the course, and measure every hole. I enter distances and the positions of all the bunkers in my notebook.

Harper ignored Danny completely. This affected Danny's play.

Missed again! It's hard to concentrate with somebody stomping around. But I must keep my tempo smooth, so—

Danny had his own way of smoothing out tensions which might affect his swing.

Oh, D-A-N-N-Y B-O-Y-D—

He sang his name to himself, slowly and in rhythm. He hit a screamer off the next tee, with no effort at all.

Wow! What a drive! Straight as an arrow, a good three hundred yards. Rhythm, and power, and timing.

Harper ignored all golf etiquette. He talked while Danny was playing.

Call yourself a caddie! That's four balls I've lost so far.

He's maybe an amateur but does he have to be a bad-mannered oaf?

The sixteenth had a plateau green.

My five iron, caddie.

Better take your four, mister.

16
170 YARDS
PAR 3

99

Arthur Partridge, Danny's manager, arrived.

*I didn't do so well, Mister Partridge.*

*Me! In the Open!!!*

*Never mind, Danny. This will cheer you up!*

*Yes, it's an entry form for the British Open. The fee and the form have to be in by Tuesday. You sign it, Danny.*

Danny was still in a daze when he met Stu Price again.

*Planning to play in the Open, are you, Danny? Well, good golf ain't enough, mate. You need a good caddie too.*

*Thanks, Stu. I'll certainly think about it.*

The Open was to be played at Royal South Downs, a famous seaside course on the south coast of England. Danny hitch-hiked all his way south, to see the course, and to play on it.

*Here we are! Royal South Downs!*

Danny was awed by his first impressions.

101

Danny met the secretary.

Can I help you, sir?

Yes. I'd like to play a round, on the Championship course.

Sorry, sir, members only. Of course, if you have a letter of introduction, or if you know a member . . .

That's it, then . . .

As Danny walked away—

I say, caddy, are you free, lad?

Caddy! Well— why not?

The senior pro at Royal South Downs was Bob Hodges.

Can I leave my clubs with you? I really came to play, but I can see the course just as well by being a caddy.

So the Brigadier nabbed you. All the regular caddies go into hiding when he appears.

Out on the course there was noisy activity.

Danny learned that all shots had to be played from the light rough at the side of the fairways.

Bally Open Championship! Fellahs hammerin' and bashin'. We members can't use the proper tees.

Not allowed to use the fairways. Bloomin' scandal I call it. Championship is still weeks away.

103

105

For two weeks Danny lived rough in an old shed, with Stu. He caddied occasionally and he practised all the time from dawn till dark.

You've got to get through regional qualifying rounds, then final qualifying rounds before you even get to play in the Open, Danny. It's a long, hard slog.

I'll make it, Stu, and by then I'll know this championship course backwards.

Sixteen on target out of twenty, and with a five iron. That's good shooting. And Danny's a glutton for practise.

Oh, D-A-N-N-Y B-O-Y-D! That keeps my swing and tempo right! And there goes ball number thirty into Stu's sack.

There's the target to keep in mind, Danny Boyd —The Open—the world's best. But you'll make it, some day!

The End.

106

# NO ONE KILLS KELSO

LIEUTENANT Larry Kelso was a very tough cop who spearheaded the war against crime in New York's 14th Precinct, mysteriously surviving every attempt on his life. His assistant was young Detective-Sergeant Bill Stone. Now they were about to pounce on a suspected drug shipment.

*Action, men! Halt all the transporters. The drugs should be in one of the first two.*

*If our tip-off is right-*

Police in plain clothes dashed out of hiding.

*Police! Hold it!*

The van broke away . . .

*We must get to the car! They're making a break.*

*We'll never catch them—*

Kelso seemed to vanish, then . . .

*How did Kelso reach the car? There wasn't time.*

*One moment he was here with me—the next, driving! He's uncanny.*

Suddenly . . .

*That'll stop you! Let's see you jump over that lot!*

There was no way for Kelso to avoid the bouncing barrels . . .

Kelso's car went over the edge . . .

. . . and into the dock . . .

Kelso's in that car! I'm going in after him . . .

A voice broke in . . .

No unnecessary heroics, Sergeant—I'm not a ghost. I jumped clear.

Kelso! You . . ? It's impossible.

Later, at Police H.Q., Captain Neam was not pleased.

So—no drugs.

We were set up. I'm going to have a talk with a certain informer.

Be careful, Kelso! The drug squad and District Attorney are not happy. During your shindig the drugs came in— somewhere else.

In the car . . .

Lurky Drang was the informer, Bill. Drop me off where I tell you.

You're the boss, Boss.

He didn't wait for me to stop! Crazy—I never saw him get out.

Down at the docks . . .

Lurky, you'd better have some good answers. No one makes a fool of me, twice.

Shadows suddenly came alive . . .

So, I've got company. Huh, you're moving out of your league.

Aaaagh! A steel bar I hit him with— It's bent!

Later, back at the waterfront . . .

It worked! Kelso's off the case. We can carry on with our drug racket.

Yeah. The guys we work for are real muscle, too big for cops to hassle.

They felt a cold wind behind them . . .

Tell me more!

Kelso! Where did you spring from?

Get him! He heard too much!

No, but I will do!

The heavy metal chain seemed to rebound from Kelso .

Aaaaagh! My hand—!

Other dockers overheard the fight . . .

Hey, what's that? In the warehouse —something's happening.

What . . ? Who knocked you about?

Kelso—he's gone! No place for him to hide . . . How much did he hear? I gotta warn someone!

Boss? Kelso was here—he knows something. He ain't giving up.

We'll take care of it.

This I owe you. I hoped you'd phone.

Kelso drove around for a while . . .

I've got company! An answer to that phone-call?

Suddenly a burst of gunfire . . .

It's a hit!

Goodbye, Kelso! Let's get out of here!

But moments later . . .

They take it for granted I've collected a funeral. Now I tail them!

It's impossible. The driver must be dead. It—they couldn't miss!

There's no one following. Back to Denson Haulage. The boss will be happy now.

Later . . .

Contract carried out, Mr Denson.

What—I I told you not to return here.

No problems. We weren't followed.

Meanwhile . . .

Kelso speaking! Send Sergeant Bill Stone and plenty of back-up to Denson Trucking Company, now! Have a warrant. Over and out!

So you weren't followed? Whose car is that? It's all shot-up!

It's Kelso's! But it can't be. We riddled him!

You crazy fools! He's tracked you here.

He can't have. He's dead. We hit him point-blank.

A breath of cold wind . . .

I have to disappoint you. Worried, Mr Denson? You should be—

Kelso! Get him!

Kelso took out the two hitmen . . .

Aaagh!

You're too slow! Now you're dead.

Kelso followed up—and dealt with Denson's two other men.

The drugs, Denson— where are they?

I want my attorney! You can't do this.

I'll ask once more . . . then you won't be around to need an attorney.

Wait—I'll tell you!

Bill Stone arrived with the back-up.

Are you all right, Kelso?

I'd say so. Drug records, import dates . . . all nicely recorded. Mr Denson has been very co-operative.

Keep him away. He ain't natural . . .

He means I'm alive, Bill. I'm kind of lucky.

At Police H.Q.
Every time you make an arrest it looks like a battlefield. The commissioner doesn't like it, Kelso.

He has the drugs, and the head man. What else does he want? I do things my way.

Bill, what kind of man is Kelso? He has the underworld scared stiff!

I'm on his side and he scares me too, Chief!

The End.

113

It couldn't have come from straight ahead!

A few minutes later, Oscar Devine and Karl Kenton raced past. They were deadly rivals of Dusty and Stan and had been suspected of getting up to lots of dirty work throughout the Rally.

Then—then it must have been a ghost car!

Having trouble, Rhodes? What a shame!

Back on the road.

That was no ghost car that forced us off the road. Was Devine behind it? Anyway, we've no time to spare!

Finally, Nubatambi, the end of the overnight stage. Jack Hagan, their mechanic, was a worried man.

What happened? You've lost your lead—Devine is one minute ahead and tomorrow's the last stage.

We had a mystery crash. But I'm going to find out who caused it.

The Rhomar was crippled.

Cant' get up any speed at all.

KLANK!

KRRUNK!

WHRRRRRNK

Next morning, while Jack repaired the Rhomar, Dusty and Steve visited the crash scene.

There's a track!

Let's look. We've two hours before the start!

Broken glass!

Not just broken glass—a mirror. Somebody set it up ahead of us . . .

Then there was no ghost car! We swerved away from our own reflection.

That's right. It took two men to carry that mirror . . . But one fell with it and cut his hand. Look—lots of bloodstains!

Back in Nubatambi.

Time's running out and we've still got to find someone with a badly-cut hand!

Dusty! Look! He could be our man!

114

115

Two of Kansala's friends came in—

He is a tiger, this one!

Non-stop attack is our only chance—

I finish you!

Right, Kansala! Who put you up to the mirror trick?

A man called Devine. He also say more money if we hold you here till after Rally starts.

Run! He will kill us all!

Thanks, Steve, good footwork.

Minutes later—

Let's hope Jack has managed to repair the car.

Hagan had everything ready—

You've five minutes till the off. The Rhomar is okay!

Thanks, Jack! It's all or nothing on this last stage now!

The last stage of the Safari got underway.

Hard right-hander coming up, Mike. Then no passing space for three miles!

Then we've got to take this car on the turn!

117

Made it! Our wheel track fitted the width of the beams—

There they are! Just ahead!

The finish post is only two miles away, Dusty.

Devine is trying to bump us off the road!

Got to keep my nerve now!

He's lost control! He watched us, not the road! He's crashed!

The victory ceremony—

Rhodes and Martin—the winners of the Cross-Africa Safari!

My name's Thomson, from Firth Motors. I'd like the pair of you and your mechanic to join our works' team.

A pleasure, sir, but excuse me a moment.

Right, you two! This time we've got you! So no more wriggling out!

Devine and Kenton were forced to confess to the Rally organisers.

You will both be banned from Rally driving for ever!

We made it on our own, Dusty. But now, driving for a works' team will be fabulous!

Yeh, we'll miss old Rhomar, but it's the start of great new adventures!

**The End**

# MANTRACKER

**B**EARPAW JAY, Blackfoot Indian and one-time sergeant of the Green Berets, trod a modern warpath, hunting law-breakers for the bounty on their scalps. One such hunt led Jay into Mexico and a risky boarding of the Chihuahua—Pacific Express as it crossed the High Sierras.

Jay went in an open window.

Ola, Conductor. Just book me to the Canyon halt.

124